PREFACE

THE present series of books has been conceived with the classroom in mind and in the hope that it will offer to students a change from what has tended to become a somewhat narrow and faded repertoire.

We have included several lesser known works of the great composers as well as some new compositions, and those standard items from the classics which are retained will, we hope, have their usefulness enhanced by the new and eminently singable translations specially made for this edition by John Morrison. We have not sought to provide books for specific classes or grades of proficiency because we realise that the latent talent in every class will respond to the demands of something exacting and, at the same time, appreciate something which can be accomplished satisfactorily with comparative ease.

We offer these books in the hope that they will fill a gap in the repertoire by providing some additional worthwhile material to sing, and that they will extend the ever widening horizons of music in schools, further education establishments and, indeed, all places where music is made.

William L. Reed

Eric Smith

London, January 1969

THE TREASURY OF VOCAL MUSIC

BOOK 3 TWO-PART SONGS

THE TREASURY OF
VOCAL MUSIC

BOOK **3** TWO-PART
SONGS

Edited by

WILLIAM L. REED D.MUS. *and* ERIC SMITH D.MUS.

BLANDFORD PRESS · LONDON

First published in 1969
© 1969 by Blandford Press Ltd,
167 High Holborn,
London W.C.1

SBN 7137 0052 1

Printed in Great Britain by
Lowe & Brydone (Printers) Ltd., London

CONTENTS

1. HE KNOWS THE HOUR
ER KENNT DIE RECHTEN FREUDENSTUNDEN

Translated by
JOHN MORRISON

J. S. BACH
(from Cantata No. 93)

12

2. WHITHER RUNNETH MY SWEETHEART?

JOHN BARTLET (1606)
Transcribed and edited by
PETER WARLOCK and PHILIP WILSON

3. TIDINGS OF LOVE
DIE BOTEN DER LIEBE

JOSEF WENZIG (from the Czech)
Translated by
JOHN MORRISON

JOHANNES BRAHMS
Op. 61, No. 4

How of - ten __ the __ blue - bird,
Wie viel schon __ der __ Bo - ten

How of - ten __ the __ blue - bird,
Wie viel schon __ der __ Bo - ten

fly - ing __ from the for - est, Has brought me __ good tid - ings,
flo - gen __ die __ Pfa - de vom Wal - de __ her - un - ter,

fly - ing __ from the for - est, Has brought me __ good tid - ings,
flo - gen __ die __ Pfa - de vom Wal - de __ her - un - ter,

4. THE FORSAKEN MAID

English version by
JOHN MORRISON

ANTONÍN DVOŘÁK Op. 32, No. 6
(From 'MORAVIAN DUETS')

Once a tur-tle-dove

Once a tur-tle-dove

from her nest, Fly-ing and seek-ing a place to rest,

from her nest, Fly-ing and seek-ing a place to rest,

Found in a li-lac tree, ha-ven for-got, Dream-ing in qui-et-ness,

Found in a li-lac tree, ha-ven for-got, Dream-ing in qui-et-ness,

L'istesso tempo

far a-way thought— Look where ___ in a sha-dy grove sits a

far a-way thought— Look where ___ in a sha-dy grove sits a

maid! She sews, ___ as she sings a sad se-re-

maid! She sews, ___ as she sings a sad se-re-

-nade, Sew - ing a ring with - out an-y

-nade, Sew - ing a ring with - out an-y

stone, Sing - ing and sew - ing, all a - lone.

stone, Sing - ing and sew - ing, all a - lone.

Tempo I

Sad - ly she sews for -

Sad - ly she sews for -

Tempo I

-get - me - not, Feel - ing for - sak - en, love dis - traught,

-get - me - not, Feel - ing for - sak - en, love dis - traught,

Sew - ing a ring with-out hav - ing a stone, Sing - ing and sew-ing it

Sew - ing a ring with-out hav - ing a stone, Sing - ing and sew-ing it

L'istesso tempo

all by her lone. Look where ___ the for-get - me -

all by her lone. Look where ___ the for-get - me -

L'istesso tempo

-not seems to fade. For - sak - en, for-sak - en —

-not seems to fade. For - sak - en, for-sak - en —

5. MY LIPS SHALL SPEAK OF THY PRAISE
(from 'BLESSED ARE THEY THAT ARE UNDEFILED')

Psalm 119 Verses 171-2
(Book of Common Prayer)

MAURICE GREENE
Edited by E. S. ROPER

My lips shall speak of Thy praise,

speak of Thy praise, Thy praise,

My lips shall speak of Thy praise, Thy praise

My lips shall speak of Thy praise

When Thou hast taught me, hast taught me Thy sta - tutes. Yea, my

When Thou hast taught me, hast taught me Thy sta - tutes.

59

tongue shall sing, shall_____ sing of_____ Thy_____ word,

mp

Yea, my tongue shall

64

mf

Yea, my tongue shall sing of_____ Thy

mf

sing, shall_____ sing of_____ Thy_____ word. Yea, my tongue shall

mf

69

word, shall sing_____ of Thy_____

sing of_____ Thy_____ word, shall sing_____ of Thy_____

6. I SING OF A MAIDEN

TRADITIONAL

PATRICK HADLEY

① Mateless and matchless ② Chose

Reproduced by permission of the publishers, Ascherberg, Hopwood & Crew

24 *pp meno mosso*

mo - ther lay, __ As dew __ in A - pril That fall-eth on the

mo - ther lay, __ As dew __ in A - pril That fall-eth on the

29 *a tempo* (♩ = ♩.) *f* *dim.*

spray. Mo-ther and maid-en Was nev-er none but she:

spray. Mo - ther and maid - en Was nev-er none but she: __

33 *pp* *poco* *ppp*

Well may such a la - dy God's mo - ther be. __

Well may such a la - dy God's mo - ther be. __

7. O LOVELY PEACE
(from 'JUDAS MACCABAEUS')

THOMAS MORELL

GEORGE FRIDERIC HANDEL

8. UNDER THE GREENWOOD TREE

From Shakespeare's 'As You Like It'

HERBERT HOWELLS

9. O WOULD THAT MY LOVE
ICH WOLLT', MEINE LIEB' ERGÖSSE

HEINRICH HEINE
Translated by
JOHN MORRISON

FELIX MENDELSSOHN
Op. 63, No. 1

40

sempre *pp*

night - fall, when you at the mo - ment   In   sleep close your eyes, it
hast____   du zum nächtlich-en Schlum - mer   ge - schlos-sen die Au - gen

night - fall, when you at the mo - ment   In   sleep close your eyes, it
hast____   du zum nächt lich-en Schlum - mer   ge - schlos-sen die Au - gen

sempre *pp*

43

cresc.

seems   That, ev - en sleep-ing, you will re - a-lise
kaum,   So wird mein Bild____ dich ver-fol - gen

cresc.

seems   That, ev - en sleep-ing, you will re - a-lise
kaum,   So wird mein Bild____ dich ver-fol - gen

cresc.

46

cresc.

My   pre-sence in   your dreams.   So   ev - en sleep-ing you will
bis   in den tief-sten Traum,   So   wird mein Bild____ dich ver-

cresc.

My   pre-sence in   your dreams.   So   ev - en sleep - ing you will
bis   in den tief-sten Traum,   So   wird mein Bild____ dich ver-

10. GO YE, MY CANZONETS

THOMAS MORLEY
(from 'Canzonets to Two Voices' 1595)

II. SWEET NYMPH, COME TO THY LOVER

THOMAS MORLEY
(from 'Canzonets to Two Voices' 1595)

12. SOUND THE TRUMPET

HENRY PURCELL
Arr. C. S. LANG

B.P.11

of joy, That skil-ful num-bers can em-ploy, To cel-e-brate, to cel-e-

joy, That skil-ful num-bers can em-ploy, To cel-e-brate, to cel-e-

-brate _ the glories of _ this day, the glo - - ries, the glo - -

-brate _ the glories of _ this _ day, the glo - - ries, the

- - - - - - ries of this day. day.

glo - - - - - ries of this day. day.

13. THE DASHING WHITE SERGEANT

Words and Music by
HUGH S. ROBERTON

Steady, rhythmically, clearly articulate, and always vital

Now the fid-dler's rea-dy, let us all be-gin! So—

Now the fid-dler's rea-dy, let us all— be-gin! So

step it out, and step it in, To the mer-ry mu-sic of the

step it out, and step it in, To the mer-ry mu-sic of the

The song should be sung through twice without pause, first with both repeats, and finally straight through without re-peats, when the first section should be '*pp*' and the second begin '*pp*' and work up to '*f*'

68

14. VENETIAN NOCTURNE
LA REGATA VENEZIANA

CARLO PEPOLI
English version by
JOHN MORRISON

GIOACCHINO ROSSINI
(from 'SERATE MUSICALI')

row! _____
sù. _____

row! _____
sù. _____

mf

And when dark-ness   comes at   last, _____ And the
Ca - ro   Bep-pe el   me vec - cie - to, no strac-

15. SPRING SONG
FRÜHLINGSLIED

ELISABETH KULMANN
Translated by
JOHN MORRISON

ROBERT SCHUMANN
Op. 103, No. 2

Allegretto *p*

1. The lark and swal-low are wing - ing, And
1. *Schnee-glöck - chen klin - gen wie - der, Schnee-*

snow - drops ev -'ry-where spring - ing. The year is turn-ing to
-glöck - chen brin - gen wie - der uns heit' - re Tag'___ und

cresc.

Spring, Sea-son of joy, and sea-son of sing - ing. One
Lie - der,___ uns heit' - re Tag'___ und Lie - der! Wie

63 choi - ces. The bells, — they are ring-ing, The cho - rus is sing-ing, For
ist es. Ent - ge - gen ihm mit Sang, — mit Sai - ten-spiel und Klang! der

choi - ces. The bells, — they are ring-ing, The cho - rus is sing-ing, For
ist es. Ent - ge - gen ihm mit Sang, — mit Sai - ten-spiel und Klang! der

66 Spring - time, for Spring-time tru-ly has come. The Spring-time, For it's
Kö - nig, der Kö - nig zie - het ein! der Kö - nig ist er-

Spring - time, for Spring-time tru-ly has come. The Spring-time, For it's
Kö - nig, der Kö - nig zie - het ein! der Kö - nig ist er-

70 Spring-time, And all can share in serv - ing, For
- schie - nen, ihr sollt ihm treu - lich die - nen mit

Spring-time, And all can share in serv - ing, For
- schie - nen, ihr sollt ihm treu - lich die - nen mit

16. VIRTUE

GEORGE HERBERT

CHARLES VILLIERS STANFORD

17. WHO IS SILVIA?

From Shakespeare's 'The Two Gentlemen of Verona'

CHARLES WOOD

Reproduced by permission of the publishers, Ascherberg, Hopwood & Crew